UNRAVELING THE "RELATIVES RIDDLE"

In order to investigate your family history, you first need to know who your relatives are. Relatives are members of your family. How they are related to you depends on what connections they have to other people in your family. The explanations below will help you understand how you are connected to the other members of your family.

GRANDPARENTS

Your mother's parents and your father's parents are your grandparents.

Your grandparents' parents are your great grandparents.

Your great grandparents' parents are your great-great grandparents, and so on.

STEP FAMILIES

Sometimes parents are divorced or widowed. If one of your parents remarries, then that person becomes your stepfather or stepmother.

If your stepfather or stepmother already has children of their own, then these children are your stepsisters or stepbrothers.

If your parent and stepparent have a baby, then that child will be your half brother or half sister.

AUNTS, UNCLES, AND COUSINS

Your father's or mother's sister is your aunt.

Your father's or mother's brother is your uncle.

Brothers or sisters of your grandparents are your great uncles or great aunts.

If your aunts and uncles have children, then these children are your first cousins.

If any of these cousins have children, then these are your first cousins once-removed.

Second cousins are the children of your grandparents' brothers or sisters (your great uncles or great aunts).

If your second cousins have children, they are your second cousins once-removed.

If your second cousins once-removed have children, then they will be your second cousins twice-removed.

PHEW! IT SURE CAN GET A LITTLE COMPLICATED!

I'M YOUR SUPER SISTER!

I'M YOUR BIG BROTHER.

WOOF!

I'M YOUR FIRST COUSIN ...

I'M SO GLAD YOU ARE!

BECOME A SUPER SLEUTH

The best way to find out about your family's past is to dig it up! Trawl through old family albums to find photos of your relatives at all different ages. Ask Mom or Dad if there are any old family home movies around that you can watch. Another terrific detective tool is interviews. You can conduct these yourself.

INTERVIEW FAMILY MEMBERS

Grandparents and older relatives can often give you the inside scoop on other family members, and are a treasure trove of interesting stories and information. Building a family history is not just about gathering names and places, you can find out amazing stories and personal details. Grab a notebook, tape, or video recorder and start interviewing family members. You can also write, call, or email them.

INTERVIEW QUESTIONS

Use a notebook or make photocopies of the list of questions below and use these to interview each family member.

1. When and where were you born?
2. Where were your parents born?
3. Where did you grow up and what was it like?
4. What were the names of your parents and siblings, and what were they like?
5. What was/is your occupation?
6. What did your parents do for a job?
7. Where did you go to school and when did you leave?
8. What do you remember most about your childhood?
9. How old were you when you got married and how did you meet your husband or wife? What was your name before you were married (if applicable)?
10. Are you aware of any family heirlooms? What are they? And why are they important to our family?
11. What has been your proudest achievement so far? And why?
12. Do you have a favorite book?
13. Do you have a favorite food?
14. Do you know if any of our ancestors came from another country?
15. Are there any great events or unusual stories about any of our ancestors?
16. Do you have any old photos, journals, letters, or papers that you can show me?

Super-sleuth Tip: It is always a nice gesture to write a thank-you note to the person you have interviewed.

The Digital Detective ...
For more ideas on interview questions and other family history research tips, ask your parents if you can visit some of the supervised internet sites, such as
Ancestory.com and
Familysearch.com

Chances are after all your sleuthing and digging you'll have enough information to fill lots of books! While you can include heaps of great information on the following pages, don't stop there! If you find you have too much information to fit in this book, why not create another book too? Then you can ask your parents to photocopy it and send it to all your relatives!

MAKE YOUR OWN BOOK

1. Use blank sheets of paper.

2. Punch holes.

3. Tie the pages together with ribbon or string.

OK, Super Sleuth. Collect the photos you have uncovered, your colored pencils, and the decorative stickers in this book, and get ready to practice your best handwriting. It's time to fill in your family history! Please turn over.

THE HISTORY OF ME

ME

THIS IS THE PERSONAL HISTORY OF

_____
(write your full name)

TODAY'S DATE (MONTH/DAY/YEAR):

MY DATE OF BIRTH (MONTH/DAY/YEAR):

PLACE WHERE I WAS BORN (CITY/STATE/COUNTRY/HOSPITAL):

THE TIME I WAS BORN:

....
AM/PM

This is a drawing/photo of me now.

MY FAMILY

This is a drawing/photo of my family.

My address is

....

....

....

(Don't forget to include any pets!) Make sure you name everyone.

MY FAVORITES

MY FAVORITE SONG OF ALL TIME IS

_____

MY FAVORITE MEAL OF ALL TIME IS

_____

MY FAVORITE BOOK OF ALL TIME IS

_____

MY FAVORITE THING IN THE WORLD TO DO IS

_____

MY FAVORITE GAME IS

_____

MY MOST TREASURED POSSESSION IS

MY FUTURE

MY PROUDEST ACHIEVEMENT SO FAR IS

_____

WHEN I GROW UP I'D LIKE TO BE

_____

WHEN I'M 20 YEARS OLD, I WILL LOOK LIKE THIS:

Draw a picture of yourself here.

The History of My Parents

FATHER'S FULL NAME: ....

MOTHER'S FULL NAME: ....

DATE OF BIRTH: ....

DATE OF BIRTH: ....

PLACE OF BIRTH: ....

PLACE OF BIRTH: ....

MY PARENTS WERE MARRIED ON (date) ....

AT (place) ....

FATHER'S OCCUPATION: ....

MOTHER'S OCCUPATION: ....

Sure, you know your parents well, but what about before you were around? What did they do? What were their lives like as children? (For more ideas, check out pages 4 and 5.) Fill in this page with pictures, letters, and stories, and write in some interesting facts about your parents.

If you have stepparents, photocopy this page, so you can fill in their details, too!

THE HISTORY OF MY BROTHERS AND SISTERS

NAME: ....

NAME: ....

DATE OF BIRTH: ....

DATE OF BIRTH: ....

PLACE OF BIRTH: ....

PLACE OF BIRTH: ....

Stick a photo or drawing
of your sister/brother here.

Stick a photo or drawing
of your sister/brother here.

Okay, so you think you know your brothers and sisters pretty well, but maybe you don't know everything about them! Ask them to fill in this page, and maybe they'll even draw you a picture for your book!

.... 'S FAVORITE THING:

Draw something here

'S PROUDEST ACHIEVEMENT SO FAR IS
....

WHEN .... GROWS UP, HE/SHE WANTS TO BE
_____

Draw something here

.... 'S FAVORITE THING:

'S PROUDEST ACHIEVEMENT SO FAR IS
....

WHEN .... GROWS UP HE/SHE WANTS TO BE
_____

If you have more than two siblings, you might have to photocopy this page, or they might have to share the space!

THE HISTORY OF MY GRANDPARENTS

What can you find out about your grandparents' lives? Are there any memories that they or your parents can share? Can you find any photos or drawings from their childhood? (For more ideas, check out pages 4 and 5). Stick pictures, letters, and stories, or write in some interesting facts about your grandparents here.

FATHER'S PARENTS

GRANDFATHER'S NAME: ....

DATE OF BIRTH: ....

PLACE OF BIRTH: ....

DATE DIED (if deceased): ....

GRANDMOTHER'S NAME: ....

DATE OF BIRTH: ....

PLACE OF BIRTH: ....

DATE DIED (if deceased): ....

Stick a photo or drawing of Dad's parents here.

DATE OF MARRIAGE: ....

MOTHER'S PARENTS

GRANDFATHER'S NAME: ....

DATE OF BIRTH: ....

PLACE OF BIRTH: ....

DATE DIED (if deceased): ....

GRANDMOTHER'S NAME: ....

DATE OF BIRTH: ....

PLACE OF BIRTH: ....

DATE DIED (if deceased): ....

Stick a photo or drawing of Mom's parents here.

DATE OF MARRIAGE: ....

Are there any other relatives' history you would like to record?
If so, record their information on this page.
(You can photocopy this page, if you have more than two.)

The History Of ....

FULL NAME: ....

DATE OF BIRTH: ....

PLACE OF BIRTH: ....

DATE OF MARRIAGE: ....

DATE DIED (if deceased): ....

What more information can
you sleuth about this relative?

(Stick pictures, letters, and stories, or write in some interesting facts here.)

The History Of ....

FULL NAME: ....

DATE OF BIRTH: ....

PLACE OF BIRTH: ....

DATE OF MARRIAGE: ....

DATE DIED (if deceased): ....

What more information can
you sleuth about this relative?

(Stick pictures, letters, and stories, or write in some interesting facts here.)

It's now time to put the results of all your detective work together to solve the mystery of your family's origins!
(Super-sleuth Clue: "Origin" means where your family comes from.)

TRACING YOUR ORIGINS

Can you reveal your family's origins? Look at the "Place of Birth" entries for all the family members you have interviewed—where were they born? What long-deceased family members did you find out about and where were they born? Where has your family been in the past and where are they now?

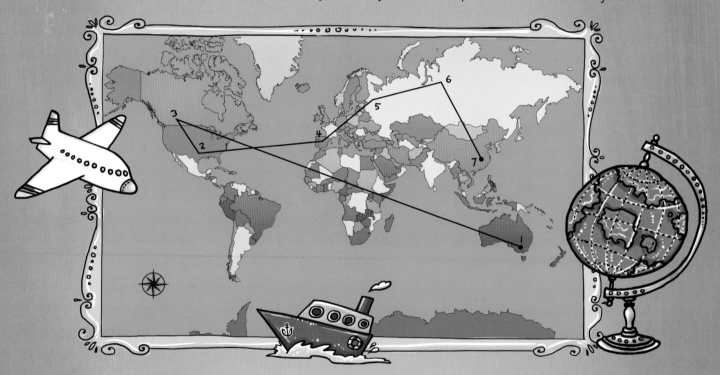

From youngest to oldest, write the names of family members below. Include their place of birth. Now photocopy a world map from an atlas. On this photocopy draw a line from the past (10) to the present (1) to track the movement of your family over time! **See above example.**

1. ....

Place of birth ....

2. ....

Place of birth ....

3. ....

Place of birth ....

4. ....

Place of birth ....

5. ....

Place of birth ....

6. ....

Place of birth ....

7. ....

Place of birth ....

8. ....

Place of birth ....

9. ....

Place of birth ....

10. ....

Place of birth ....

FaMiLY IDENTiKiT

Aside from being related to each other, family members often have other things in common. In the course of your sleuthing, have you discovered any common family traits? These could be shared physical traits, common sayings, or beliefs—these similarities make up your family's unique identity!

PhYsiCAL FEATuRES

In some families, everyone might have great-grandpa's ears or the female members might have Aunt Tessie's rosy cheeks. Look at photos of your family members, what common physical traits can you see?

OuR COMMON PHYSiCAL TRAiTS ARE:

Stick your evidence here!

SaYiNGs OR PassioNs

MY FAMiLY'S FAVORiTE SAYiNG:

MOST/ALL OF MY FAMiLY LOVE:

MY FAMiLY FLAG

What beliefs, passions, hopes, and dreams do you and your family share? What colors and patterns do you think best represent your family? With everything you now know about your family, what would a flag of your family look like? Design your own family flag here!

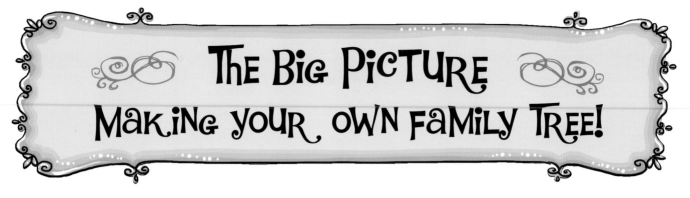

The Big Picture
Making Your Own Family Tree!

With the information that you have found out, you should now be able to fill out the Family Tree poster in this book. Making your own Family Tree poster will help you get the big picture about how you and your family members are related to each other.

How to Create Your Family Tree Poster

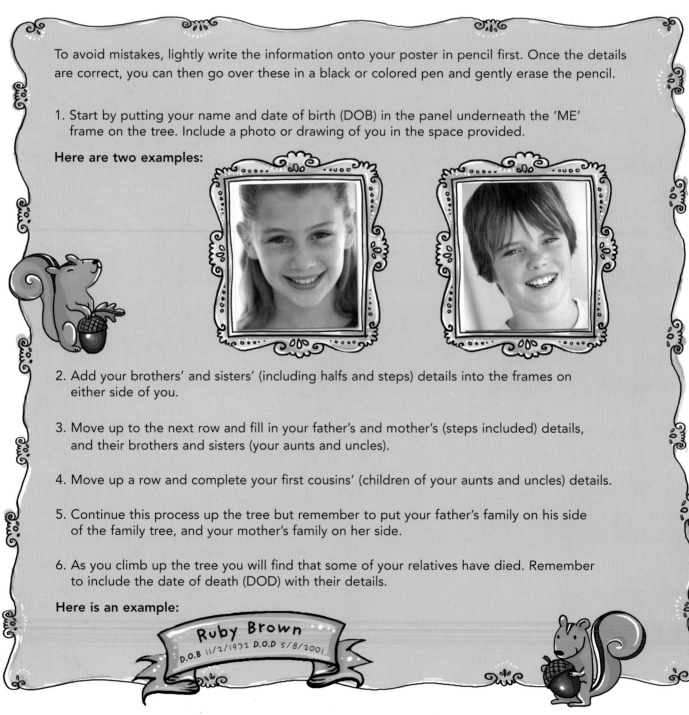

To avoid mistakes, lightly write the information onto your poster in pencil first. Once the details are correct, you can then go over these in a black or colored pen and gently erase the pencil.

1. Start by putting your name and date of birth (DOB) in the panel underneath the 'ME' frame on the tree. Include a photo or drawing of you in the space provided.

Here are two examples:

2. Add your brothers' and sisters' (including halfs and steps) details into the frames on either side of you.

3. Move up to the next row and fill in your father's and mother's (steps included) details, and their brothers and sisters (your aunts and uncles).

4. Move up a row and complete your first cousins' (children of your aunts and uncles) details.

5. Continue this process up the tree but remember to put your father's family on his side of the family tree, and your mother's family on her side.

6. As you climb up the tree you will find that some of your relatives have died. Remember to include the date of death (DOD) with their details.

Here is an example:

Ruby Brown
D.O.B 11/2/1932 D.O.D 5/8/2001